155

★

THE
★ *STORY OF* ★
SILENT NIGHT

★

★

NOVELS BY

PAUL GALLICO

The Snow Goose
The Lonely
Jennie
Trial by Terror
The Small Miracle
Snowflake
The Foolish Immortals
Love of Seven Dolls
Ludmila
Thomasina
Flowers for Mrs Harris
Mrs Harris Goes to New York
Too Many Ghosts
Scruffy
Coronation
Love, Let Me Not Hunger
Three Stories
The Hand of Mary Constable
Mrs Harris, M.P.
The Man who was Magic

GENERAL

The Steadfast Man: A Life of St Patrick
The Hurricane Story
Confessions of a Storyteller
The Silent Miaow
The Story of Silent Night

FOR CHILDREN

The Day the Guinea-Pig Talked
The Day Jean-Pierre Was Pignapped
The Day Jean-Pierre Went Round the World

★

THE
STORY OF
SILENT NIGHT

★

Paul
Gallico

783.65
G

★

Crown Publishers, Inc. · New York

PROLOGUE

𝕿his is a story where truth is already touched by legend and research is coloured by imagination. Can anyone say for certain who is destined to be famous? And why should there be a note in history of the son of a poor Austrian weaver or the bastard of a musketeer serving in Salzburg? Who could foresee in a young country priest and a humble schoolteacher-organist the stuff of romance and the seeds of genius?

Yet one hundred and fifty years have not erased the memory of Joseph Mohr and Franz Gruber, respectively poet and composer of the Christmas hymn *Silent Night*. A number of facts have come to light concerning their origins, lives and deaths. Yet there are long periods of silence in the histories of both which invite speculation to fill in the chinks where research runs into the dead end of events now forgotten or distorted. However, imagination is aided by the fact that there are counterparts of these men living today in the same rustic backwaters where they flourished.

If one knows something of the villages and country towns of Austria, one feels closer to them for there the yesterdays are not so far removed. Progress in Europe has spread irregularly, leaving here and there odd little pockets which have remained almost unaltered through several centuries. Such are the towns of Oberndorf and Hallein and the hamlet of Arnsdorf, all in the immediate neighbourhood of Salzburg. The tempo of life is little changed from the days a century and a half ago when Gruber and Mohr dwelt there. No one, least of all themselves, ever expected that they would leave an indelible and unforgettable mark upon the hearts of millions.

Here is how I believe it to have come about.

P.G.
Monaco, April 1967

★

THE
STORY OF
SILENT NIGHT

★   ★

★

★

THE STORY OF
SILENT NIGHT

" 'Twas the night before Christmas, when all through
the house,
Not a creature was stirring, not even a mouse. . . ."
(Clement C. Moore)

But on the night of 23 December 1818, in the little Austrian town of Oberndorf near Salzburg on the banks of the frozen river Salzach, a mouse —so the story goes—did stir.

He not only stirred, but he invaded the organ loft of the Church of St. Nikola with its onion tower, reminder of the days when the Turkish tide had washed up that far to the west. There, because he was a cold mouse and a hungry one, he perpetrated a deed and initiated a chain of events that was to resound to the farthest corners of the earth.

It was the following morning, which had dawned crisp and clear, Christmas weather with the snow lodged a foot high on the sloping roofs of the houses, that an important gentleman in a blue frock coat, flowered waistcoat, white stock, beaver hat, and woollen muffler wound about his neck, crunched the five miles that separated the tiny hamlet of Arnsdorf from Oberndorf. By a side door he entered the Church of St. Nikola, took off his coat and sat down at the organ to run through the programme of hymns for the midnight Mass that evening.

[1]

His name was Franz Gruber, a dark-haired man of about thirty-one, with a pleasant face and somewhat long nose, cleft chin and a touch of humour about his mouth. The world had never heard of him but in the small ponds of the two neighbouring communities he was a very large frog indeed. In Arnsdorf, which was hardly more than a wide place in the road, he was the schoolmaster and sexton and in Oberndorf-on-the-Salzach, the organist. By day he taught the children of Arnsdorf in the schoolhouse where he lived above the single classroom, and as sacristan of the church functioned at baptisms, weddings and funerals as well. On Sundays and holidays, when there were services, he went to Oberndorf to provide sacred music.

He flicked his coat-tails, adjusted the organ bench and pulled out the stops. Then, with eyes closed and head thrown back in anticipation of the first thunderous chords he would evoke, he trod the bellows pedals and pressed the keys. But no music issued from the pipes, only a soft, breathy sigh. Something was very wrong.

Before Gruber had time to investigate this unhappy phenomenon he heard a sound by the door and turned to see his friend Joseph Mohr, the young priest, himself a musician. Mohr was in Oberndorf on a temporary basis as assistant to Father Joseph Nostler, the permanent priest of St. Nikola, who was out at the time.

Gruber said, "*Grüss Gott*, Joseph," and then, "Heavens! What's happened to the organ?"

Mohr—he was then twenty-six, with merry eyes and a gay, boyish air which somehow did not seem to match the long and sombre soutane—

raised his arms in a helpless gesture and said, "A catastrophe! Come along and I'll show you. When old Nostler finds out he'll blame that on me too." The priest and his assistant did not get on.

He led Gruber to the loft behind the gilded stand of pipes and pointed to the hole and the rip leading from it in the worn leather bellows. "I discovered it this morning after early Mass, when I sat down to play for myself a little. A mouse must have gnawed a hole during the night; look, there are the droppings. At the first pressure the whole thing gave way. Look how old and rotten it is—it should have been attended to long ago," and then he added, "It's hopeless."

Gruber inspected the damage with genuine anguish. "And the organ-mender won't be coming up from the Zillertal until the snows have melted in the spring," he cried.

A Christmas Eve Mass without music was unthinkable. He fingered the split leather and said, "Here's a fine fix! What's to be done?"

Rather timidly, as the two men walked back into the church to contemplate the now mute and useless organ, young Father Mohr said, "Well, I had an idea while waiting for you to come, I have written a little poem. Here . . ." and he produced a bit of paper from his soutane and then, coughing and correcting himself, "Well, actually not a poem, perhaps, but some words for a song and it seemed to me that if . . ."

The schoolteacher, startled, said, "A poem?" and then smiling at his friend said, "That doesn't surprise me. You were always more of a poet than a preacher and a singer, perhaps even more than a poet. Why you ever chose the cloth . . ."

[3]

The shy and pleasant expression faded from Mohr's face as he replied shortly and with grim asperity, "It was chosen for me." And Gruber regretted his levity, remembering the strange story of the boyhood of this somewhat misfit, itinerant priest whom Fate seemed to send hither and thither to fill any temporary vacancies but never acquiring a parish of his own.

"And besides," Mohr added, still angry, "it isn't *that* kind of a song."

"Of course not," Gruber soothed his friend, and apologized further, "I meant nothing more than that your talents are numerous."

But both were aware of what lay behind Mohr's reference to "that kind of a song". It was just that it was well known that he enjoyed raising his fine tenor voice with the river men in the wood-panelled *Bauernstube* of the inn. Oberndorf was a port on the navigable river Salzsach, in those days an important commercial thoroughfare. When it was *Bockbier* time or the *Heurige*, the strong, heady new wine flowed, the sailors foregathered in the tavern at night, zithers twanged, bawdy songs were sung.

As a matter of fact Father Nostler, a sour and crabbed man, had already put in a complaint to the Archbishop's Consistory in Salzburg about his assistant. In his letter he drew a picture of Mohr going about like a wild student with long tobacco pipe and pouch, evidencing a preference for music and musical entertainment rather than his breviary and consorting with low sailors who sang ditties that could not be considered uplifting. This was not the type of man to look after the spiritual needs of the congregation and he asked to have him transferred. Fortunately an investigation by the Dean of the Cathedral established that for all of his gaiety and love of life and people, Mohr carried out his duties, was particularly conscientious about bringing comfort to the sick and was liked by most of the community. So for the moment no action was taken on Father Nostler's charges.

"But about this poem, then," Gruber continued, "or whatever you wish to call it," and he paused with a look of enquiry.

Mohr, his anger now fled, said almost apologetically, "Well, I only thought that since there is not a note to be had from the organ and you are almost a virtuoso on the guitar, I wondered if you might not be able to arrange something—let's say in two parts for your voice and mine, perhaps a chorus for the children, with guitar accompaniment. If it were simple they could learn it quickly and we might have it ready for tonight."

Gruber was again surprised. "Guitar in the church? On Christmas Eve?" he queried, and already envisioned the expressions of shock and disapproval on the faces of the congregation and more fuel to Nostler's fire. And yet he had thought when he had been confronted with the organ damage, "Needs must when the devil drives." So he said, "Perhaps one might. Let me see what you have written."

Gruber took the paper and read the first stanza, and ever more rapidly carried along, those that followed. And as he did so a queer chill ran down his spine. It was indeed not *that* kind of a song. On the contrary. It seemed to lay its hand upon his heart and speak to him gently, simply and movingly and he looked up in utter astonishment at his friend who stood there with the diffident air of one totally unaware that he had produced anything extraordinary.

Gruber was both stirred and puzzled by the words. Whence had they come? From where within this gay, light-hearted, seemingly irresponsible young man who always seemed to have either a joke or a song on his lips and never a serious thought? What was there about them that was so strangely compelling?

"Stille Nacht! Heilige Nacht!
Alles schläft; einsam wacht."

The very first two lines immediately seemed to exercise an hypnotic effect upon him and already he found himself listening to the faint sounds of music waiting to be born. He was both confused and excited.

He stammered, "Y-yes, I understand. The guitar accompaniment kept simple and the children could sing the last line of each stanza in four part chorus. Let me take it home and see what I can do." For he wished now to be alone with the words that Joseph Mohr had written, to give himself up to the spell that the poem in its innocence and simplicity had begun to weave about him. He clapped his hat hurriedly upon his head, wound his woollen muffler about his neck, said, "I'll be back as quickly as I can," and set off through the snow for his home in Arnsdorf.

The characters of the two friends, Mohr and Gruber, could not have been more antithetical, and at the time of the incident of the Christmas

Eve crisis, the priest appears as the more robust and dramatic figure of the pair. For he was a bastard born of a musketeer, Joseph Mohr, who simultaneously deserted his mistress Anna Schoiberin, a seamstress in Salzburg, and his army, and was never seen or heard from again.

In accordance with the customs of the times, the boy born of this union on 11 December 1792, was allowed his father's name but his start in life was neither auspicious nor enviable.

To begin with there were problems connected with the baptism. No one could be found willing to stand sponsor for this unfortunate by-blow, the third in the life of a poverty-stricken woman. Eventually one Franz Joseph Wohlmuth offered himself for this rite but was compelled to send a substitute to the font, for he himself was forever barred from crossing the threshhold of the church by his gruesome profession. Franz Joseph Wohlmuth was the official hangman and executioner of Salzburg.

As is often the case with illegitimates, the child was talented, intelligent and attractive. As a boy of eight or nine, he had a stroke of luck—probably the only one of his entire life. His voice and charm brought him to the attention of Johann Hiernle, an important priest in charge of the Cathedral choir. Hiernle took him under his wing, opened his house to him, became his foster-father and undertook his education.

Mohr developed a fine tenor voice. He was taught to play the violin and organ, and thus was rescued from what otherwise would have been an existence of abject squalor and drudgery. But there was also a price to pay. He was unable to command his own destiny, since he owed his good fortune to Father Hiernle who had him marked for the Church. For two years he attended the Seminary at Salzburg, again thanks to his foster-father, for bastards were not ordinarily admitted to this school, and on the 21 August 1815, the boy whose heart all through his student years was filled with the joy of life, gaiety and fun was ordained a priest. He was a most unlikely one. Also he had a further handicap. Never strong, he had weak lungs and lacked the stamina to handle a church on his own.

This was the man whose trifling little verses written to cope with an emergency Franz Gruber now clutched in his fingers as he hurried home-wards and like deaf Beethoven, tried to listen to the harmonies already clamouring within him.

Gruber's beginning had been of undistin-guished placidity when contrasted with the origin of his friend. He was born on 25 November 1787, the third son of a weaver of Hochburg, close by the Bavarian-Austrian border. They were poor; their cottage tumbledown. Like Mohr, Gruber was talented musically and this leaning divided his family. His father considered it a waste of time for a boy who was to become a weaver; his mother, more sympathetic, abetted him in secret lessons given by one of those wonderful characters which every Austrian village in those days seemed to have—organist-choirmaster-schoolteacher, Andreas Peter Lichner.

The boy progressed famously but without hope of any future other than the weaver's chair. The elder Gruber had no use for music.

And then, as they so often do in this story, Fate

and Chance took a hand. When Franz Gruber was twelve years old, Peter Lichner fell ill and there was no one to play the organ in the church on Sunday. No one, that is, except Franzl, who sat at the console, his feet barely reaching the pedals and to the astonishment of all, played the High Mass. Bursting with pride at the praise showered upon his son, father Gruber not only withdrew his objections but delved into the family sock and invested five *Gulden* in an old spinet so that the boy could practice.

Further, he was sent to Burghausen for two years to study with Georg Hartdobler.

In 1806, already an accomplished musician, he attended technical school and a year later secured the position of teacher at the village school of tiny Arnsdorf. In this humble post he remained for twenty-one years.

Even Gruber's first marriage lacked the romance on which epic narrative may be built, for it was more a succession than a saga. He wed the widow of his predecessor, acquiring simultaneously a wife, several offspring, and the late husband's job as sexton and choirmaster. When she died he married another Arnsdorf girl, and later, once more widowed, married a third time.

It was in 1816 that he secured the additional post of organist in St. Nikola's Church in the neighbouring town of Oberndorf. And there he made the acquaintance of the ebullient young priest, Joseph Mohr.

Music in the 18th and 19th centuries in Europe was an almost universal diversion. It could be indulged in by great and lowly alike. Amateurs gathered together in the villages, towns and cities in string trios, quartets, sextets. If one could not afford to own an instrument one could always sing and devotees blended their voices in four part motets, cantatas, madrigals, carols or folksongs.

When one thinks of the amount of music that was "made" throughout the German and Austro-Hungarian states in those times in the great cities such as Frankfurt, Dresden, Leipzig, Budapest, Vienna, Cologne, Mannheim and Berlin, it is astonishing that only the giants such as Bach, Handel, Haydn, Mozart, Beethoven, Schubert, Schumann and Chopin survived. Music-makers by the thousand flourished. Yet they were insignificant and their works are either non-existent or unremembered. How much more hopeless of immortality then was the unassuming organist who sat at the console of the parish crossroads church.

For Mohr and Gruber, music was a mutual language. They probably played four-handed Bach and Handel on the organ, or duets on their "*Zupfgeigen*" or "pluck-violins", as guitars were known in their times.

Nor was composition a great mystery. Mohr handing Gruber his lyric and expecting a setting back that same Christmas Eve would have surprised neither. For one of the aptitudes of any competent musician was improvisation. He could sit down at the pianoforte, harpsichord or organ without notes and play whatever melodies or harmonies came into his mind. Down through the years Gruber would have whiled away hour after hour alone in the church, simply letting his fingers wander over the keyboard and allowing the music to flow.

[10]

At Arnsdorf there is yet another onion-domed church, the *Wallfahrtskirche Maria*, where Gruber performed his various duties as sexton. The *Volksschule* stands in its shadow. Here he both taught and lived. He entered the door and was hardly aware of walking through the empty classroom, garlanded for Christmas, past its painted desks and the green tiled porcelain stove at the far end with its curious ceramic-studded, clay hemisphere at the top. There was not a soul about, for the children were already on holiday.

He climbed the wooden staircase to his spare and simple study with its well-scrubbed deal floor, the stove, a desk and a few pieces of hand-painted furniture, as well as the ubiquitous carved figure of the crucified Christ on the wall.

His guitar hung from a peg too, but he did not take it down. He went instead to his spinet which occupied the most prominent place in the room, and without removing his overcoat sat down at it and re-read the poem of Joseph Mohr, born Joseph Nobody.

He said it to himself out loud:

> "Stille Nacht! Heilige Nacht!
> Alles schläft; einsam wacht.
> Nur das traute heilige Paar.
> Holder Knabe im lockigten Haar,
> Schlafe in himmlischer Ruh.

> "Stille Nacht! Heilige Nacht!
> Gottes Sohn, o wie lacht
> Lieb' aus Deinem göttlichen Mund
> Da uns schlägt die rettende Stund,
> Jesus in Deiner Geburt.

"Stille Nacht! Heilige Nacht!
Hirten erst kundgemacht
Durch der Engel Alleluja
Tönt es laut bei fern und nah:
Jesus der Retter ist da!"

What gripped him was the simplicity of its narration of the story told and retold every Christmas Eve of that starlit night in Palestine when all Bethlehem was asleep, and only the Holy pair Joseph and Mary kept lonely watch on their Newborn in the manger. Mary sang to Him as mothers always have—"My darling, my curly-headed boy; sleep in heavenly peace."

Yet he could not linger too long. Gruber tried to collect his musical thoughts and sounds he had been hearing ever since he first read the verses, but he was still in too much of a state of agitation. He touched several chords on his instrument, played half a melody and ceased in irritation as a loud peal of bells from the tower of the neighbouring church broke in upon his reflections.

He arose and went to the window to look out upon the snow, the stone crucifix outlined in white rising from the churchyard and down the village street some children pelting one another with snowballs. As if in echo to the peal now ended, borne upon the winter wind Gruber heard the bells of the Church of St. Nikola in Oberndorf, but rendered soft and gentle by distance. In place of the unrelated jangle of clapper upon bronze they seemed to convey a rhythm that was peaceful and soothing.

Three mummers in the guise of the Three Kings passed by below, but Gruber did not even see them, for lost in meditation he was gazing across the whitened, flat lands with prosperous farms and fat, peak-roofed houses. Smoke drifted upwards from a chimney, a few desultory snow-flakes fell from the sky and his lips framed the words, "*Schlafe in himmlischer Ruh*"—"Sleep in heavenly peace".

No more than a dozen years before fires from burning homes and hayricks had illuminated the night, gravestones had sprung up over the countryside like weeds as the armies of Napoleon ravaged the land. The French had fought the Austrians and when the invaders had gone, the Austrians had made war upon the Germans.

But that, too, had come to an end and one could sleep now, child and man, in heavenly peace. Once more he heard the faint strains of the bells of St. Nikola. He knew so well the tone of each one, their sequence and their rhythms. Yet now, blending in with his reverie and feelings, they seemed to hold the suggestion of a melody. And as he turned from the window to the spinet on which lay Mohr's poem, it was as though he saw clearly for the first time. He discarded all the grandiose musical ideas he had been fermenting and murmured:

"How stupid of me! What pompous thoughts I have been having. Why, it's only a lullaby— Sleep my child and rest; I am watching over you this silent and peaceful night—the kind of song to which cradles have been rocked and restless infants quietened to sleep for centuries."

He had found the key now to the composition, the simplicity needed to match the words. No complicated harmonies or exalted effects were

[13]

called for but only the unadorned melodic line to bring to the minds of the listeners something of the mood of that December eve in Bethlehem in the long ago.

Soon a sheet of paper was covered with a rough score. Gruber played the notes and sang them to himself, then took his guitar from the wall and transcribed the accompaniment. It was all done swiftly and easily since what musician worthy of the name was not capable of putting together a plain, homespun, cradle song? Gathering up his papers and slinging his guitar over his shoulder, Gruber set forth on the return journey to Oberndorf, hoping that Mohr would think he had done the right thing with his unpretentious setting to the poem.

"What, back so soon, Franz?" Mohr said, amazed, for noon had hardly struck and the priest was just about to sit down to his lunch. He invited Gruber to join him and, over a bowl of hot soup, the two men studied the notes, Mohr nodding and humming. Gruber was as modest about his music as his friend had been about the words.

"You will see how it struck me," he said. "Perhaps I haven't done justice to your poetry, but we will try it out when we have finished eating and see whether you like it."

"No, no," Mohr assured him hastily, "you have surprised me. Your melody is far superior. After all, my idea was only to help us over our difficulties . . ."

An hour or so later, the two men were contemplating one another and the hastily written score with the satisfaction that comes to creators

[14]

of any calibre when endeavour has managed to work out fairly smoothly. The blending of their two voices to the guitar pleased them. If the refrain chorused by the children came out as well, the music for that part of the service following the reading of the Christmas story as told by St. Luke in Chapter II, verses 1–14 of the Gospels, would be adequate. And "adequate" was how they thought of it.

That afternoon there were collected in the priest's study beneath the wreaths and garlands of evergreen, six little boys and six girls, scrubbed and shining in their warm woollens, jackets and pinafores. They had been selected as the most talented of the children's choir of St. Nikola and the most likely to learn quickly, for now there was not much time left. And once more the character of the gay young priest who had summoned them became apparent when the girls appeared with red and green ribbons braided through their plaits and the boys wore them in the shape of rosettes at their stockings. Mohr had supplied streamers of the same colours to be attached to Gruber's guitar. The schoolteacher-composer's thoughts must have been along the lines of: "Well, in for a penny, in for a pound," for he only smiled and picked up his guitar which had suddenly become more Italianate than Austrian, and after he and the priest had sung a verse they rehearsed the children.

"So now: Hannes, Evchen and Peterli, you sing like this—'Ta-ta, ta ta-ta-ta-ta . . .' And you, Gretel, Liesel and Johann sing—'Da-di, da di-da-da-da . . .' Michel, Lotte and Maria, here is your part . . .'' and Gruber handed them the counterpoint. "Franzl, Sepp and Inge—yours goes just the opposite . . . First we'll try each group singing separately. Very good. Now we will put them all together. Ready then, and remember, I want to hear the girls at the end of the first line . . . *Also dann—eins, zwei, drei—*"

The voices of the children blended:

> "Schlafe in himmlischer Ruh!
> Schlafe in himmlischer Ruh!"

The two men glanced at one another again with satisfaction. A little rough. A bit of trouble with the third bar of the repeat, but easily remedied. The silent organ and the rip in the frayed bellows were no longer important. Two journeymen workers, a minor poet and a minor musician, in a few brief hours had managed to arrange a passable substitute.

Christmas Eve in the Austria of 1818 was very different from the holiday celebrated in the West today. It was then a serious and devout religious festival, solemnized far more in the churches even than in the homes. The family-made *crèche* with its carved or waxen figures of the Holy Family was more important than the Christmas tree. Prayer, reading of the Gospel and the sacred music were at the heart of the ceremony. True, there were also gifts and feasting and the children would already have been scared out of their wits by the appearance of St. Nicholas accompanied by his assistant known as the "*Grampus*", who seemed to know all about their sins. But the climax was the midnight Mass.

That night it was cold and fine. There was a crust on the snow and underfoot it was so dry that it crunched and squeaked beneath the heavy boots of the churchgoers wending their way to the service at St. Nikola. Their cheery *"Grüss Gotts"* as they met and joined up with one another rang through the stillness. The air was sharp and crystal clear and crackled in the nostrils. The stars seemed to hang from the sky and one of particular brightness, if you looked in just the right way, appeared to be shining as though attached to the top of the tallest pine near the church. Successive families as they passed would look up and then point it out to those who followed.

Once more the bells pealed forth from the tall, whitewashed steeple. Within, hundreds of tapers and candles reflected from the gilded and silvered plates and chalices, the brightly painted figures of Saints and Virgins, softening the faces of the stiff, Gothic, wooden Madonnas and haloed figures, endowing them with gentle grace. Angels, cherubim and seraphim and all the Holy Ones of the Catholic Calendar of Saints were decorated with pine boughs and hollyberries.

Ordinarily, Gruber would have been at the organ, softly playing in the congregation to the strains of old hymns. Now the worshippers were aware of the unusual silence as they entered and heard the shuffle of their own feet on the stone floor. But word had got around very quickly of the catastrophe and there was much buzz of conversation and wonderment as to what was to replace it. True, the choir might sing *a cappella*, but well—that wasn't real Christmas Eve music.

The people packed themselves close on the hard

[17]

benches, the men in their sombre, lumpy best clothes, the women with gay aprons over their dark skirts, coloured shawls about their shoulders and bright scarves on their heads. The rough river men in the inland sailor's garb of the times of red and blue, occupied the rear pews.

The smoke of incense drifted upwards to the roof of the nave, the coughings and scrapings ceased as old Father Nostler, as solid and grim in his robes as the figures carved by peasants out of wood, began the conduct of the Mass. Where the organ should have played its part, the choir chanted from its loft, yet those in the church felt how much the music was missing. It was like meat without salt. Only a few noticed that the assistant priest, Joseph Mohr, was nowhere to be seen.

Father Nostler read the appropriate Epistle to Titus, II and the lines from St. Luke, Chapter II, verses 1–14. From the pulpit the priest had spoken feelingly enough of the miracle of the birth that had taken place some eighteen hundred years ago, its meaning to mankind and the hopes that it had brought to all the miserable and enslaved of the world.

When he finished, the slap made by the closing of the great Bible echoed through the silent church as though it had been a signal, as indeed it was. For this was the place where he had been told the children would appear and sing. However, he was not prepared for the surprise as Joseph Mohr, Franz Gruber and the twelve youngsters, the organist with his guitar slung from his shoulder, marched in from the vestry and ranged themselves before the altar.

When the crusty old priest saw the manner in

which all were decked out, his face was almost apoplectic and he raised his hand as though to bring proceedings to a halt. But it was too late, for Mohr had already stepped forward and was saying in effect: "You all know that through the accident to our organ, which happened only last night, we have been denied our usual music. However, Herr Gruber and I have prepared a little Christmas song which we hope will take its place."

There was a momentary rustle of astonishment and excitement. In the rear pews the river men grinned and nudged one another as though to say, "Good old Mohr! Trust him to come up with something." Then as Gruber shifted his instrument into position, silence fell once more. He plucked the first chord from the strings of the guitar, and the tenor and baritone voices of the priest and the schoolteacher filled the church, harmonizing as they sang in slow tempo the sweetly lulling melody of the opening words: "*Stille Nacht! Heilige Nacht!*"

The fresh young voices of the children picked up and twice repeated the refrain, "*Schlafe in himmlischer Ruh!*" the light, childish soprano of the girls first soaring to the roof beams; the second time pronouncing it as softly as a benediction. Verse followed verse; chorus after chorus and when the last line was sung: "Jesus the Saviour is here!" there was heard a long drawn out sigh and a murmur of satisfaction. There was not a member of the congregation who was not moved by the haunting notes of the refrain.

Father Nostler was not amused. Frowning and muttering to himself and not even deigning to look at his assistant, he took over the altar to complete the rites of Communion and then, his fury unappeased at what he considered a sacrilege in content and execution, he retired to his quarters to pen yet another outraged letter to the Bishop of Salzburg.

Gruber and Mohr, however, stationed themselves outside the door of St. Nikola's to greet the emerging Oberndorfers. The reactions were mixed.

The wife of a Selectman gushed, "It was a lovely service, Father, but we did miss our music, didn't we?"

An elderly woman, tight-lipped, remarked, "Really, Father, it seems to me that church is not the place for playing a guitar."

One of the sailors gave the young priest a dig in the ribs, "Not bad, but we could have done with something a bit more lively, eh?"

A man complimented Gruber, "That was a nice melody. But haven't I heard it before somewhere?"

Another family stopped to say, "Thank you, Father, How pretty the children looked."

Gruber remained somewhat cynically amused, but on the whole pleased for the majority of the comments indicated that they had managed to get away with it. He murmured to Mohr, "So far, so good. But I don't think old Nostler was very pleased. I hope there won't be any trouble."

Mohr laughed and replied, "Oh, he'll get over it!"

When the last of the worshippers had dispersed behind the clouds of their own breath in the night air, Gruber wryly held out his hand to his friend and said, "Merry Christmas, Joseph!"

The intonation was not lost upon the priest who grinned back at him impishly, "The same to you, Franzl."

The two men shook hands and Gruber set off for Arnsdorf and home once more, still smiling gently beneath the muffler now wound about his face to the eyes.

A few days later, as the townspeople began to look ahead to the coming new year and what it might hold for them, the incident and the song to which it had given rise were totally forgotten.

𝕿he verdict of time upon manifestations of genius is unpredictable. Works by creators in every field of the arts who at some moment or other feel that they are inspired and have produced something immortal, languish rejected by critic and public alike. Trifles tossed off to pay a bill, to amuse a child or even efforts about to be discarded because they seem ordinary or unworthy often achieve imperishable fame.

Franz Gruber was for his day a competent journeyman musician who, when he died, left behind some ninety compositions mostly of a religious nature and as modest, unpretentious and undistinguished as himself.

Each time he sat at his spinet, clavichord or pianoforte during his life's span, he set out to write the very best music he could. All contained some of the essence of the man, his dreams, his imagination, his hopes for survival. Yet of these major productions, but one Mass for mixed chorus and small orchestra is still occasionally heard in Germany today. During his lifetime he once rose above himself and soared like a lark upon one heavenly and never-to-be-forgotten flight. And when he put together a simple melody, he was wholly unaware that he had created anything in the least remarkable.

On the contrary. When some thirty-six years later Gruber was asked for his account of how the song came into being, he wrote in his own hand a few cold, dry-as-dust sentences pertaining to the event:

"It was on the 24th December of the year 1818 that the incumbent assistant priest, Father Joseph Mohr of St. Nikola's Church in Oberndorf, handed over a poem to the organist of that church, Franz Gruber, who at the same time was also school teacher in Arnsdorf, with the request to write an accompanying melody for two solo voices, chorus with guitar accompaniment. The latter, in accordance with the appropriate request of this holy man who was himself a musician, handed over his simple composition and it was performed that Christmas Eve to general approval."

Even then, so long after when it had begun to work its magic and the authorship of Silent Night was being attributed to the world's greatest composers, Gruber was not impressed. He had not even the vanity to use the first person in his meagre narrative but wrote about the church organist Franz Gruber as though he were observing him coldly from a distance. His only reaction to the universal pirating of his song and its appearance designated as "authors unknown" in dozens of publications, was a grumbling that somebody had tampered with two or three bars and changed a few notes. His was simply the approach of a professional musician. For the rest he never deemed it worth bothering about.

Thereafter in that testament he declares: "Mr. Joseph Mohr, who was the author of this poem and many other religious songs, died on the 4th December, 1848, the worthy vicar of Wagrain in Pongau." And this was all he had to say of his collaborator.

Of the "many other religious songs" of Joseph Mohr, not one has remained. The words of Silent Night have been translated into more than fifty European languages alone, not to mention those of the New World, Asia and Africa.

The priest rather fancied himself as a would-be poet. His friends often teased him and dubbed him poet-jester, and one suspects that perhaps his efforts on most occasions were more doggerel than poesy.

Mohr had been embarrassed when he handed the verses to Gruber, and for a reason of which he was probably not even aware. In the creation of those lines something had happened to him which never had before, and nor ever would again. They had burst from his heart all in one sudden outflowing like a freshet. Another hand seemed to have taken hold of his pen.

Poets often long for inspiration and then when on rare occasions it manifests itself are more than likely to be fearful and mistrustful of it. Mohr was afraid that Gruber might laugh at him when he read what he had written.

And in all probability what held these two men from the realization of what they had wrought was that each saw it only from his own angle and experience, one as a writer and the other as a composer. Each unaware had contributed only half a miracle and therefore saw the whole as nothing miraculous at all. Would Mohr's verses have survived without Gruber's composition? Would Gruber's melody be remembered had it not been for Mohr's words?

And why and how did this seemingly insignificant song survive at all?

Ｔhere is a famous old hymn, the first lines of which are:

> "God moves in a mysterious way,
> His wonders to perform."

And this would indeed seem to be true of the rescue of Silent Night from the oblivion to which it appeared to be consigned, since its original impact upon the world was no greater or more significant than a single grain of sand in a desert.

God seemed to move in a strange and complicated manner to enable this particular little work of liturgical song to live on, to carry its message of love and extraordinary heartache throughout the world. And the first hint was to be found in the closing lines of Gruber's own account.

This clue was but a passing reference and never would have been included in Gruber's hard-facts narrative had it not been, as indicated before, that somebody down through the years had tampered with his composition. His only interest was to set the record straight, which he did with a sheet of music which accompanied his story and which is the only extant version today in Gruber's own hand.

He concluded his statement:

"As this Christmas song came into the Tyrol by means of a well-known Zillertaler and which, however, appeared in a song collection in Leipzig somewhat altered, the author of same has the honour to include herewith a score following the original melody."

But who was the "well-known Zillertaler"?

He was a virtuoso, maned like a lion, bearded like Jove himself, a large, lusty and powerful personality.

In the town of Fügen in the Zillertal, under the shadow of a jagged, snow-topped range of Tyrolean Alps, lived the Mauracher dynasty, builders of organs.

The Maurachers were not only manufacturers and repairers of the most expensive and important musical instrument of the times, but were also musicians. To build an organ properly, to construct the pipes in perfect pitch, you had to be able to play. Before the newly finished product was despatched to the church for which it was intended, its thunder first rang through the halls of the Fügen factory to the majestic chords of Bach, Handel and Buxtehude.

In the year 1819, the travelling Mauracher was organist Karl and in April when the snows blocking the roads had melted and begun their rush to the sea, and the first purple crocuses confirmed that spring was indeed at hand, he hitched up his team to his wagon. Filling it with his tools, sheets of leather, spare pipes, pedals, stops and wire he clapped his feathered hat upon his massive head, hung his long curved Austrian pipe from his mouth and set off upon his round of visits to churches that had written to complain of sick or disabled organs. And, of course, the Church of St. Nikola at Oberndorf was on his list.

It was not until the middle of May that Karl Mauracher pulled his team to a halt there to be greeted by the hearty, "*Grüss Gott und will-kommen!*" of Franz Gruber.

By then Joseph Mohr was no longer there. Whether finally the fulminations of his enemy Father Nostler had their effect in Salzburg, or that his luck had run out is not known. The climate of Oberndorf suited him well and he would have liked to have remained there. But this was not his pattern and he was now at one of the ten insignificant posts he would fill, one after another, before he was finally tucked away for good and all in the oblivion of the tiny mountain village of Wagrain.

Dismounting, Mauracher followed Gruber into the organ loft and gave a great snort as he saw the rip in the bellows. He fetched his tools and settled down to patching it, no doubt letting drop a few words of sales talk and the value of installing a new instrument rather than relying upon one that could suddenly let one down, and at the most inconvenient times.

As a travelling man, the organ-mender brought news too, social and political, from gossip of the neighbouring towns to the uneasy peace that had settled upon Europe now that Napoleon was no longer there to menace it, though there was no telling how long those barbarian Bavarians to the north would remain quiet. Still, times were better; even those Colonial wars in the Americas seemed to have come to an end. He went on to say he had heard that in Vienna Beethoven had completed his Grand Mass in D, and the composer was supposed to be working now on a Ninth Symphony, of all things embodying a chorale. Mauracher had met him once—an unpleasant fellow but unquestionably a good musician.

Gruber listened silently. Arnsdorf and Oberndorf had little or nothing to contribute to the march of events.

The job completed at last, the two men went around from behind the organ loft into the church, where Mauracher seated himself at the console, air was pumped up into the renewed bellows and to the delight of Gruber's ears a Bach Toccata and Fugue filled the building.

And then suddenly, in the midst of a resounding phrase, Mauracher stopped, turned to Gruber and asked, "When was it you said your damage occurred?"

"The morning of Christmas Eve."

"I thought that's what I heard," said the Tyrolean. "Whatever did you do for music, then?"

This was the first time that anyone had inquired about the now forgotten Christmas Eve musical crisis.

Gruber smiled in recollection. "Well, it was a little unusual. Do you remember Mohr, the chap who was here as assistant priest then? No, I don't think you ever met him. He was something of a versifier and a musician, too. We both—ah—

used to strum the guitar. Well, he wrote a little poem and I set it to music. We sang it with a children's chorus. It was scored for two male voices—tenor and baritone, that is to say Mohr and myself, with guitar accompaniment. You should have seen the faces of the congregation when we entered the nave. But it seemed to go down well." And now he smiled again, "At least the whole bizarre business was quickly forgotten."

Mauracher looked astonished. "What a combination! I never heard of such a thing. I should like to see that."

"Goodness!" Gruber laughed, "I wouldn't know where to begin to look for it, or where Joseph put it, if it hasn't been swept out already. *Sagen Sie mal*, Frau Schneider . . ." and here Gruber addressed a stout *Putzfrau*, the cleaning woman who was passing through with her bucket and mop, "Did Father Mohr leave any papers behind anywhere, other than those in the music cupboard? I know it isn't there, because I only recatalogued our library recently."

Fat Frau Schneider reflected. The church was full of corners, crannies and chests. She suggested, "There would only be that old closet behind the vestry where he used to keep his clothes and his guitar."

"If you like," Gruber offered, "I'll have a look." A moment later they heard him shout, "Ha!" as amidst old bits of paper, half-written scores and hymnbooks without covers, crumpled and dusty, he retrieved the manuscript of the poem and music.

Returning, he handed it to the organ-mender who placed it on the music rack before him, pulled out the stop of the *vox humana* and tentatively fingered the melody, his lips moving as he read the words.

"You see," said Gruber, "it's nothing."

"We-ell," Mauracher replied, and showed his teeth through his bushy beard in a curious kind of smile, "Wait!" He eyed the score once more, then began opening stops until he had activated the whole noble range of the pipes. He threw back his massive head and with an accompaniment as though rendered by an orchestra of flutes, viols and trumpets, filled the church with the hymn until the beams of the roof shivered.

He grinned at Gruber. "It has something, hasn't it, old fellow?"

Gruber laughed. "*YOU* have something, my dear master. You could make a five-finger exercise sound like a Handel Hallelujah."

Mauracher said, "You might let me have a copy."

Gruber only laughed again and said, "Take it with you, if you like. No one here will have any further use for it, since you have mended our organ so perfectly."

Mauracher nodded, stuffed the score inside his coat pocket, shouldered his bag of tools and patches and climbed onto the driver's seat of his wagon. "If the Elders should decide upon a new organ," he shouted as he drove off, "don't forget us," waved and Gruber watched him out of sight, and along with the only extant score of Silent Night, out of mind.

When, some three months later, Mauracher returned to Fügen, the incident had dimmed, overshadowed by other events of his trip: an order for a great new organ to be built along the most modern lines, plus more news of the world outside of their valley, the political troubles brewing in the north, in Saxony and Brandenburg.

He came upon the crumpled score once more among his papers when he unpacked. He meant to show it to the choirmaster; he meant to play it for his wife and children; he meant even sometime to make an organ transcription along the lines of his improvisation. But as so often happens, life and the immediate took over. The song was not heard from again for three years.

In the year 1822, Kaiser Franz Joseph I of Austria and Czar Alexander I of Russia, during one of those political intimacies which in the Europe of the nineteenth century were to spell life or death for so many marching infantrymen, came to Fügen as guests at the castle of Count Ludwig von Donhoff. And one evening the Count had some of the locals up to entertain his Royal visitors. Amongst these were the family Rainer, the precursors of today's famous Austrian Trapp Family singers. In their repertoire was Silent Night. Their Majesties were delighted, so much so that the Czar invited the singers to St. Petersburg.

And here, strangely, the flame dies out again for ten more years.

It is said that the Rainers continued to spread the song and even took it with great success to America. Yet they do not appear again in its strange career. Perhaps their function was solely to receive it at some time or other from the hands of Karl Mauracher, maybe at one of those moments of violent spring cleaning, where Frau Mauracher tackling the mess of manuscripts in a cupboard threatened to throw the lot out unless her husband did something about them. Thus the song would have come to his attention again and he could have passed it to this group.

Yet the ears and the hearts of people might still have been unprepared. It is quite possible that had the song been published then, it might never have accomplished that for which it was destined.

Silent Night was next heard from through another family, the *Geschwister* Strasser, a quartet consisting of two brothers and two sisters from Laimach in the Zillertal. Laimach and Fügen are neighbours and again we are back in the Tyrol.

In addition to their yodelling and peasant *Schuhplattler* dance, which included a great deal of stamping and rump slapping, the Tyroleans were famous throughout Teutonic Europe as the fountain head of Austrian folk-song. They were both a fashion and a fad and when they appeared in their native costume and sang their sentimental mountain songs, they were received enthusiastically. Everyone in the Tyrol seemed to sing. And here again one faces the mystery of design. Would the song have caught on ever by itself if rediscovered as the creation of two unknown men? Or was it the fact that it made its bow to Europe as a Tyrolean Folksong, "Authors Unknown" that gave it its initial impetus, the appeal of something primeval?

It would remain "Authors Unknown" where Silent Night was concerned for some forty years or more following its creation. Yet the names of the

Strasser Quartet have come down to us. The two girls were Amalie and Karoline, the boys Andreas and Pepi. They were not professional singers like the Rainers, but glove makers. Some of the finest chamois and kidskin gloves were exported from the Tyrol to the great annual Leipzig Summer Fair. When the Strassers brought their winter's work there, the *Geschwister* would earn a little extra money by giving modest concerts of Tyrolean folksongs. And by then Silent Night was in their repertoire too. It had become a native creation, belonging neither to Mauracher (if he remembered) nor the Rainers, but to the country. Authors would only have been an embarrassment to authenticity.

They sang it for the first time in Leipzig at a small affair in 1831 as one of a group of four indigenous carols. A new character in the design made a brief appearance, Franz Ascher, organist of the Royal Saxon Court Orchestra. He was in the audience, found the song enchanting and invited the quartet to return the following year in December and sing it at the Christmas Mass which would be held in the Royal Chapel at Pleisenburg nearby.

The family was delighted to accept such an honour. The thrifty glove manufacturers worked hard on a consignment for Christmas sale and the four singers arranged and advertised a concert of their own the same month in the ballroom of the Hotel Pologne. The notice appeared in the *Leipziger Tagesblatt*, where it triggered an anonymous letter, another strand in the fine skein that was being woven. Had one single thread been severed. . .?

"Greatly Honoured Sirs:

"Having seen the announcement in your valued newspaper pertaining to the concert of the *Geschwister* Strasser from the Tyrol, might it be in order respectfully to request them to include the little *Weihnachtslied* "*Stille Nacht*" in their programme. I had the pleasure of listening to them sing it last year and would enjoy hearing it again.

"Yours faithfully,
"AN ADMIRER."

The four were delighted to comply. It was added publicity and guaranteed them at least one paid admission. But it was not a question of one, but of how many could be packed into the hall. It was an ideal seasonal entertainment and an opportunity to hear the quartet known to have been invited to sing in the King's chapel.

And now the time, the place and the audience were right, with one more important character waiting in the wings for his cue to enter the story and play his part.

Once more, the four Strassers, the girls fresh-faced, their dark hair looped in braids about their heads, clad in bright coloured dirndls with contrasting aprons, the boys in green trousers, foresters' jackets and frilled shirts, blended their voices in their rendition of their Tyrolean Christmas song. Only this time it was different.

For it *was* Christmas time that night, without and within and this was, amongst other things, not a church but a concert hall. The Christmas spirit was abroad. In the homes there was the smell of roasting goose, sugared fruits, *Lebkuchen* and *Weihnachtsstollen*, the traditional holiday cakes, pine boughs and hollyberries. It was the time of mysterious comings and goings behind closed doors, packages and the whisperings of excited children. For the Germans it was the most endearing and sentimental season of the year.

As for that important player who had been awaiting his summons? He was already there in the fourth row, sitting spellbound. His name was Anton Friese and he was a Dresden music publisher in Leipzig briefly on business. To while away the last evening before returning to his home and holiday celebration with his family he had on impulse, as he passed the Hotel, purchased a ticket and taken his seat.

Perhaps it was the very urban smartness and sophistication of the members of the audience in the face of the unexpected that enabled the simple song to pierce directly to their hearts, evoke long forgotten memories of childhood, of innocent days spent in the little villages and farms of their youth. It had a nostalgia that seemed to bring back all the love and tenderness of Christmases past to combine with that of their own children of the present.

When the last note had died away the audience sat silent, still enchained by the mixture of emotions evoked. Then the pent up feeling overflowed into a storm of applause and the quartet was compelled to repeat the number. And this time Herr Friese was ready. For at the first hearing he had been too overwhelmed by the thoughts and recollections the song had aroused in him to do more than listen and know that his eyes were moist.

Extracting a pencil from his pocket, he turned

over his programme which had merely listed, "TYROLEAN CHRISTMAS FOLKSONG. Authors Unknown", and on the back drew the five lines in treble clef. As he listened for the second time he jotted down the words and in a kind of of musical shorthand of his own, captured the notes of the melody as well.

That night at his hotel, he transcribed the entire song perfectly—or, that is to say, almost perfectly except for one or two slight lapses of memory that were to irritate the composer in the years to come and eventually supplant the original.

The Christmas song returned with him to Dresden and in 1840 appeared for the first time in print, published by Friese under the title, *Four genuine Tyrolean songs sung by The Brothers and Sisters Strasser from the Zillertal*. It was scored for four voices and there was a second version for piano and single voice. This was fine publicity for the Strassers, as well as giving the song authenticity and cachet. (What the family Rainer had to say about this is not recorded.) Shortly after it was noted in a Catholic song book and then was glibly pirated from collection to collection. In 1844 it had travelled to Berlin where it was published by Finck in *Musical Home Treasures of the Germans*, thence lifted to Dr. Gebhardt's *Musical Youth's Friend*, and in 1848 to the same publisher's *Musical School Friend*, but always credited as a Tyrolean or Austrian folk-song of unknown origin.

In all likelihood the Strassers never knew who had written it and Herr Mauracher had either forgotten or at the time he handed it over to the

Rainers, did not deem it important. And since no name appeared on the original manuscript there would have been no source to check.

And now the song began to travel from Leipzig, Dresden and Berlin; like a stone thrown into a placid pool, the circles made by the modest hymn spread ever wider. It went south from Frankfurt, Mannheim and Stuttgart, north to Hanover and Hamburg and crossed the borders of the Low Countries to Utrecht and Amsterdam. Prague and Vienna knew it and it was heard as close to its original home as Salzburg.

On Christmas Eve when the candles of the tree were lit, it was sung by families in humble homes and in the proud courts of Dukes, Princes and Electors. The village choir sang it to organ accompaniment and it began to be performed as well at the Mass celebrating Christ's birth in the big cathedrals of Europe.

And now that it was becoming so familiar, interest in its origins had been roused and it was being ascribed variously to Kaspar Aiblinger, the Bavarian court conductor and church composer, Ludwig van Beethoven, Mozart, Franz Joseph Haydn and his younger brother Michael Haydn, and a number of other well-known contemporary musicians.

During this time how fared the two men who actually had written it?

Wagrain today is a ski resort in the Niedere Tauern in the shadow of the Arlberg, gay, light-hearted, colourful with its hotels, chalets and winter slopes alive with tourists and holiday-makers. In the early part of the nineteenth century it was a collection of a few peasant huts and cowsheds and a small, poor chapel that could not even boast one of the more affluent onion-topped towers. It was also the end of the line for Joseph Mohr, the restless, soldier's bastard and priest with the soul of a poet.

After having wandered for some ten years from parish to parish, he came there at last as Vicar in the year 1828 and remained for twenty years.

He departed as destitute as he had been born, for it was noted that he left nothing behind but a worn and much darned soutane and his prayer book. There was not even money enough to bury him; he was interred at the expense of his community. All that is remembered of him is that he was loved, that the early fires of his youth subsided; he tended his flock, comforted the sick, presided at baptisms, marriages and deaths, instructed the young and served his parish of stolid country folk to the best of his ability. His only pleasure was an occasional night in the *Bierstube* with the cowmen, but as the years dragged on he sang less. Always weak in the chest, in the winter of 1848 he was called to administer the last rites to a dying woman on a distant farm. Returning home he caught cold, pneumonia followed and he died.

Not so much as a badly executed oil, or even a pencil sketch of him existed when fame finally found him. And when at last in 1912, they went to exhume his poor remains to place his skull in the hands of a sculptor to enable the artist to reproduce something of what he might have looked like, for a bust destined to appear in a memorial chapel, not even his grave could be located. The cemetery had fallen into neglect; tombstones had been overturned or made illegible by harsh winter storms and there was nothing to denote remembrance of Mohr. Careful research and enquiry was necessary from still living old people who finally identified the spot.

Franz Gruber was more fortunate. For twenty-five years he was a square peg in a round hole, a musician compelled to serve as schoolteacher, while exercising his real profession only when doubling as organist.

In 1833, however, he succeeded to the post of director of the choir and organist of the principal church in Hallein, a thriving market town on the river Salzach not far south of Salzburg. There he lived the not uncomfortable life of the bourgeois professional man whose compositions were achieving performances. He sired twelve children, of whom two surviving sons and daughters did him honour by following in his footsteps with musical talent.

His, at least, was not wholly a voice crying out in the desert. He was heard. He wrote music, Masses, chorales and scored them for instruments; they were occasionally sung and played. He had increased both the size of his puddle and his own stature therein. He was a man worth the efforts of a painter and both a portrait of him in middle life and photographs taken in old age survive. He died in Hallein in 1865, at the age of seventy-eight.

Were these two men ever aware during this time of the resurgence of the creation of that long-ago Christmas Eve? There is evidence that its appearance in one or another of the song books came to the attention of both Mohr and Gruber. Yet neither of them ever of their own volition laid claim to authorship.

𝕿here are two stories told of the eventual disclosure of the real authors of *Silent Night*. One is in all likelihood apocryphal. It relates how the King of Saxony, intrigued by the anonymity of the carol and suspecting the song to be of more modern composition than the composers to whom it was attributed, sent his *Hofkapellmeister* as a musical detective through Saxony and Austria making enquiries at every little village church or musical group. Eventually he was supposed to have tracked down Herr Gruber in Hallein and embraced him, calling him master and genius. Unhappily there is no evidence to bear it out.

Far more endearing is the other and probably true tale, involving yet another Royal Person, His Majesty King Friedrich Wilhelm IV of Prussia, in which certain facts are documented. Also it involves what might appear to be a stretch of the long arm of coincidence. This was one of the kind which may not be used in fiction but actually every so often takes place in life.

Late in 1854, choir director P. Ambrosius Prennsteiner of the Benedictine Monastery of St. Peter in Salzburg, which was also a famous music school for the training of choirboys and choristers, sat in his office close by the extensive music library and studied a letter passed on to him by the Abbot. It was a request from the *Kapellmeister* of the King's orchestra in Berlin for a copy of the score of the Christmas song *Stille Nacht! Heilige Nacht!*

by Michael Haydn, if one were available. His Royal Master had heard the song and wished it performed on Christmas Eve. It was understood that Herr Haydn, younger brother of Franz Joseph, had written this hymn and since for forty-three years up until his death in 1806, he had been employed as *Kapellmeister* in Salzburg, where he had written more than three hundred and fifty compositions for the church, the original orchestration might be preserved there.

Father Ambrosius did not relish the prospect of searching through voluminous bundles of scores or *Partituren*. Nor did he remember a song by that name amongst those of the younger Haydn. However, the request of his honourable colleague in Berlin called for a reply.

There were a number of choirboys and students working in the library and the Choirmaster summoned one of them into his office. "You, Gruber, come here a moment."

Coincidental? Only perhaps in the accidental choice of the boy summoned. The children of Franz Gruber of Hallein were talented and one of the youngest, Felix, who later became a teacher and Professor of music, had been sent to school in St. Peter's in Salzburg for training. His presence there on that date is a matter of record.

The monk handed over the letter to him saying, "Here, read this—*Stille Nacht! Heilige Nacht!*—Go and look through all the works we have of Michael Haydn and see if you can find it."

Young Felix Gruber read through the letter and gave a snort, "Huh! Michael Haydn never wrote that song. My father did."

The Choirmaster looked shocked. "What's that

you're saying? Your father? Oh, come now, Gruber!" For he took it to be boyish boasting. He knew of Franz Gruber and his reputation as a competent enough musician who had yet to produce a work of a calibre to be attributed to a member of the great Haydn family.

"But he did," the boy insisted. "Because we all know about it in the family. Papa wrote it years ago before I was born, before he went to Hallein, with a friend of his—a priest, when the organ broke down. They sang it on Christmas Eve with father playing the accompaniment on his guitar. Nobody had ever done that in a church before."

The monk was in a quandary. This was no idle boasting, the boy spoke with simple conviction. He said, "Are you sure about this, Felix? Why if he—and you say a priest—wrote a song of sufficient importance to be ascribed to Michael Haydn and rate a performance by the *Hofkapelle* in Berlin, has he never claimed his rights?"

The boy replied, "No one ever asked him. Once a new song book came to our house and Silent Night was in it ascribed to 'Authors Unknown'. Papa just laughed, and then said they couldn't even get the notes right."

"Mmm," said the Choirmaster, "Well then, if what you say is true, perhaps your father should be the one to deal with this, eh? If, indeed, he wrote the song he ought to be able to make them a copy." And he threw a sharp glance at the student. If he were exaggerating, or even telling a lie this would be most certain to bring it to light.

But young Gruber was not in the least taken aback. "Yes, sir," he said, "I'm sure he'd be pleased to do so. Will you send him the letter?"

Father Ambrosius was satisfied. It seemed an excellent way to kill two birds with one stone. The request of the *Herr Kapellmeister* would be honoured and if Michael Haydn was wrongfully being credited with the work of a contemporary composer living less than a dozen kilometres down the river south of Salzburg, well then, it was time that this obvious injustice was corrected.

Not long after, the Director of His Majesty the King of Prussia's orchestra in Berlin was surprised to receive a packet from Hallein in Austria, a town he had never heard of before. It contained a sheet of music entitled, *Weihnachtslied*, but scored for full orchestral accompaniment: strings, flute, bassoon, clarinet, French horn and organ. Enclosed with it was a letter containing exactly the same modest, third person, factual account of its composition that Gruber later wrote for his family, beginning:

"It was on the 24th December of the year 1818, that the incumbent assistant priest, Joseph Mohr of St. Nikola's Church in Oberndorf, handed over a poem to the organist of that church, Franz Gruber . . ."

Gruber's version was produced on Christmas Eve to His Majesty's great satisfaction and every Christmas thereafter, until the King became incapacitated. But if there was so much as a thank-you note from Berlin's *Kapellmeister* it has not been preserved either in the family of Gruber's descendants or the archives of the little Gruber museum in Hallein. Song books and publishers merrily continued to credit verses and melody to the unknown recorder of Austrian or Tyrolean folk music.

It was not until 1867 that an Austrian printer, Durlicher, published a handbook on Pongau, that district of the Niedere Tauern Alps embracing St. Johann and Wagrain, in which the then resident priest of the latter village states that Joseph Mohr, his predecessor, wrote the words to *Stille Nacht! Heilige Nacht!* and Franz Gruber of Hallein, the music. *This was the first ever written acknowledgement of either.* And by this time both men were dead.

In the meantime their innocent Christmas lullaby took flight and girdled the world.

It became a thing of extraordinary power with a life of its own. Besides the fifty or more languages of Europe, it spoke in every foreign tongue from Hindi, Punjabi and Tamil to Philippine Tagalog and Ethiopian, from Kurdish, Turkish and Japanese to a dozen African tribal dialects. Christian Arabs, Malays, Chinese, Australian aborigines and Eskimos began to sing it. It was heard in Catholic cathedrals and Protestant churches.

The Rainer family had first taken it to the New World, but it was the German immigrants of the mid-nineteenth century, escaping from religious persecution, who spread it far and wide over the Republic of the American States. For when they fled they carried their song books tucked into their meagre baggage. On Christmas Eve on the high seas, in the fœtid holds of immigrant sailing ships, families brought out their accordions and zithers and lifted their voices in the song that was bound up with the tenderest memories of all they had left behind.

They scattered north, south and west and the German Christmas with its festive tree, their customs and their music went with them. Once more Silent Night was on the move.

It was heard in the cold bivouacs during the Civil War when for the Yule night North and South called truce and the fraternal enemies across the trenches joined their voices.

The melody was plucked from the banjos of the pioneers westward bound, camped within the circle of their covered wagons. It was chorused by the slaves on Southern plantations and played on a mouth organ by a lonely cowpoke riding fence on his tired cayuse, with the stars of Christmas night drawn like a mantle about his shoulders.

Missionaries took it across the Pacific to the islands of the South Seas, to Indonesia, the Malay peninsula, the Empire of Japan and the walled cities of China. In the packs of Franciscans, Jesuits, Baptists, Methodists and Presbyterians, it penetrated Africa. The Eskimos heard it from the trappers and traders. In the west this simple creation extended its sway over agnostic and atheist, as well as Christian and Theist.

And along with the wild-fire spread of the carol and at last its acknowledgement as the work of a nineteenth-century Austrian priest and Bavarian-born organist and schoolteacher, there came screeching, trumpeting and squalling, a rag-tag and bobtail gaggle of carpers and critics who attacked not only the song, but its authors from every possible angle. They tore into the work and demonstrated first that neither Mohr nor Gruber could have written it. Then with equal facility they proved that they did, but plagiarized it from an earlier Latin verse and a folk melody originating in the vicinity of Hochburg, Gruber's birthplace.

In 1897, George Weber, *Kapellmeister* of Mainz cathedral, attacked the song as lacking the slightest indication of either Christian or any other religious thought, as doing injury to the beliefs and Christian feeling with regard to the Holy Mary and the Holy Foster Father to designate them as a wedded pair. He condemned the entire poem as more fit for a Punch and Judy show. The music he characterized as completely monotone without emotional content, refinement or interesting themes. Lumped together he dismissed the whole business as tasteless, cheap and sentimental slush.

Defenders arose to say that Mohr and Gruber had never intended to produce a great work of art, and its faults could be forgiven on the score of their simplicity. The Gruber family took a hand, reacting violently to the further accusation that not Gruber but Mohr himself had written the music to his own verses.

Into the breach stepped one Andreas Winklers, with a message from an old friend. In a letter to the *Salzburg Chronicle* this gentleman from Tamsweg wrote:

"Your Honour:
    "Often invited as a student with others to visit the hospitable and most honourable *Herr Vikar* Joseph Mohr in Wagrain, it used to be our custom when we were stimulated, to toast the poet of Silent Night. He

[45]

would thank us and declare that one of the happiest moments of his life was when shortly before Christmas of 1818, he said during a meeting with *Herr* Franz Gruber, 'Let the two of us put together something for Christmas Eve. And that's exactly what happened. I wrote the text and Franz Gruber the melody.' Those were the never varying words of *Vikar* Mohr."

The critics persisted. Professors of music, organists, orchestra leaders, composers, lexicographers, writers, literary bigwigs and long-nosed bigots joined in the fray throughout Germany and Austria denigrating the efforts of two unpretentious men who had not profited by so much as a single sou, who had never asked for anything and who never pretended that they had done anything than the best they could at a particular minor crisis in their lives.

The only ones who loved what they had wrought, whole-heartedly and unreservedly were people. And they numbered millions. Blackest sin of all against Things As They Ought Not To Be, this love was experienced by unbeliever as well as believer, Muslim, Buddhist and nature worshippers, red, white, yellow, brown and black. It crossed the religious lines of the Christian whites as well as the infidel and became a symbol of the one day of the year dedicated to peace on earth and good will to men.

The power of this random collection of words and musical notations is mysterious, its hold upon so many in the world unfathomable. Christmas is an invention, a solstice of pagan importance now adopted to commemorate the birth of a God as determined by Canon Law, and so it is celebrated with service, with prayer and music, hymns, carols and invocation of the Divine. This was the purpose for which Silent Night was written.

What the censorious have found unbearable about it is that in addition to suggesting a picture of a holy and miraculous birth, it gives rise to a host of other emotions, feelings and longings. It has an unexplained underlying sadness and evokes an unsatisfied yearning for the kind of beauty and goodness that in the end always seems to elude us. It is as though we were compelled to look into a mirror to see there the children we once were when first it entered our homes and lives, and to reflect upon what we have become. For even as some of the critics have bitterly complained, more than a religious song it is a picture of a family idyll.

Music and words touch on some secret melancholy chord so that its listeners are never far from tears. "Maudlin!" yapped the Teutonic hatchet men. "Is this indeed so?" asked one later defender. "It is true, the song is soft and sentimental. But is it a sin to have a gentle and compassionate heart? Is it wrong to be possessed of a soul?"

Eventually it began to dawn upon its detractors that they were pursuing a butterfly with a cannon. This bright-winged song was never meant to be a concert piece for percussion and cymbals or to match the symphonic polyphony of the masters of music. It was intended to be sung in a small church and from thence it entered the home where on the most tender night of the year, families gathered with their children. It never tried to loom larger. And yet how big it has become.

At last the baying of the pack pursuing the two innocents resting peacefully in their graves subsided. The nineteenth century gave way to the twentieth and with it came honour and recognition for Joseph Mohr and Franz Gruber. Plaques and reliefs blossomed on walls, memorials were erected, museums opened, new grave markers were wrought and the simple and sometimes pathetic memorabilia collected to which might cling some of the magic from two men who never professed to have any.

It was difficult in the case of Mohr, because there was so very little of him left. No one had cherished him enough in life to care to remember his lonely death. He had so few possessions to leave and no one to inherit what there was. Not even his name was his own.

It was not easy to arrange a shrine for him, or assemble the few relics by which he might live again in the eyes of a visitor. But there was the modest cottage in Oberndorf which had once served as the Vicarage to St. Nikola and now adjoins the small memorial chapel raised to the memory of the men.

For a small fee an ancient peasant Granny jingles the keys at her belt, unlocks the door and shows you the room where that ecclesiastical bird of passage lived during his brief tenure there as assistant and chief gadfly to grumpy Father Nostler.

Her grandmother must have known Mohr personally and probably disapproved of his wild ways.

The chamber contains the truckle bed on which he slept, a chest of drawers handpainted in gay colours in Austrian style and a table on which reposes his rosary, his Bible and prayer book, a candlestick, a crooked pipe, a jar and a tobacco pouch. And those are the remains of Mohr.

If he were to return today he would not recognize the bronze bust of himself which, with that of Gruber, occupies a niche in St. Nikola, nor the character of the young priest painted on the iron fretwork over his grave, nor the saintly old man depicted in stained glass within the memorial chapel. For it is not even certain that the skull exhumed from the cemetery at Wagrain was his. Everything he ever was has been obliterated with the exception of some verses of a song.

Gruber was more fortunate. He had a large family and a measure of fame. Upon his passing his wife (who survived him by ten years), and his children saw to it that things that had impinged not only upon his life, but on his work were preserved. These are now a permanent memento in the Silent Night Museum in Hallein. There you will see his pianoforte, his desk and chair, his inkwell, his pen, the kind of notepaper he used for his compositions, the manuscript of the song, the famous Halleiner version of 1854 and original of the very one he copied and sent to the *Kapellmeister* in Berlin. And further to bring him to life there is the guitar he played in the church at Oberndorf to accompany his friend, himself and the children.

On the wall hangs a portrait in oil of the musician whose fingers once plucked the strings of the now mute instrument. He is clad in a bottle-green coat. His green waistcoat has tiny roses embroidered upon it and he wears a blue stock upon a white shirt. His eyes, a peculiarly light brown, gaze out of a nineteenth-century face, long nose, long sideburns, unruly hair framing a high, broad forehead, cleft chin and humorous, sardonic mouth that seems to say, "Well, and now here you are. And you've had to pay admission, too. Where were you all a hundred years ago?"

During the last century and a half Oberndorf, Hallein and Wagrain have changed, but Arnsdorf has never stirred. In that little tucked-away corner of the world yesterday and tomorrow are as one. The schoolhouse adjacent to the church, except for the plaque over the door, is exactly the same as it was when Gruber taught there, even to the benches and desks in the classroom, the green porcelain stove and the scribblings on the blackboard.

The plaque reads:

> "Stille Nacht, Heilige Nacht
> Wer hat Dich o Lied gemacht?
> 'Mohr hat mich so schön erdacht
> Gruber zu Gehör gebracht,
> Priester und Lehrer vereint.' "

For this a free translation might be:

> "Silent night, Holy night,
> Oh song, who made you?
> 'Mohr created my words so beautifully,
> Gruber brought the melody to life,
> Priest and schoolteacher together.' "

Somehow even more touching than the things at Hallein are Gruber's quarters upstairs over the classroom, exactly as they were when he lived

and worked there for so many years. The spinet
that was there then is still in place, the same
crucifix hangs upon the wall and there is the
painted furniture and desk. But amongst the
relics are those that bring us closer to him; papers
he corrected of pupils long gone and the framed
report of the school board upon his application
for the job of teacher. Succinct and reveal-
ing it reads: "Musical knowledge of extraordinary ability in all branches, particularly as
organist."

Nothing else has altered except that today a
school-mistress in a red and blue dirndl is there
in the place of Gruber in his flowered vest and
bottle-green coat, and if you were to visit you
might find her giving a lesson on the zither in the
late afternoon in the empty classroom to a girl
with two long yellow braids. Gruber too, gave
private music lessons in this manner and you
might expect almost to see him at the school, or
plodding down the road on his way to Oberndorf.
For as the village was in times past, so it still
looks and feels today, as the peasants there go
clothed practically as they did then, the whitewashed homesteads unchanged.

Oberndorf has expanded somewhat more.
Many new houses have been built but it, too,
seems to live on memories, for the river Salzach
is no longer a thoroughfare or an artery of trade,
and the sailormen whose rough songs and hearty
beer carousels were such an irresistible temp-
tation to a gay young priest, are gone. The new
church built in 1902 on a site further away from
the river, looks exactly like the old and its
interior is identically glittery with saints and

martyrs, gold and silver twisted columns, stained glass and religious paintings.

Not far from the vicarage where Mohr dwelt is an old mill and a tall, square water tower dating from the year 1540. The millstream has vanished, but there is a pool which at one time must have been connected with it. In it lie some trout idly fanning their tails, ignoring the alien goldfish drifting by. In a photograph taken before the century's turn, this water tower is visible adjacent to the original baroque Church of St. Nikola which has now disappeared, pulled down after damage by one of the Salzach floods. On its site the Silent Night Memorial Chapel was built in 1937. The structure is ugly and uninspired, resembling more a small mausoleum than a building that should remind one of something that has brought pleasure to so many millions of people. Hexagonal in shape, bullet-domed with its shingle-roof porch, its interior is no less disappointing. There is a wood carving of the Nativity over a tiny altar and two stained glass windows respectively idealizing Mohr and Gruber.

And yet once a year this edifice undergoes a transfiguration, and if there are such things as restless spirits and the surviving souls of men wandering the invisible planes, it will be to this place that the ghosts of Joseph Mohr and Franz Gruber will return on Christmas Eve. For here it is when the snow is on the ground again that the living Christmas trees surrounding the Chapel are festooned with lights and the stars descend to crown them. On the very spot where originally it was heard, Silent Night is sung as it was that very first time.

There could be no more touching performance. For on that one night Franz Gruber's guitar is removed from its case in Hallein and brought over to Oberndorf where, as they did in 1818, its strings vibrate again and provide the background for the voices of children of the town, many descended from those first twelve, singing to Gruber's music and the words of Mohr of the birth in Bethlehem. There are singers, too, at Mohr's grave at Wagrain, others where Gruber lies in Hallein, and yet another group intones the hymn at the schoolhouse of Arnsdorf. Simultaneously the song echoes in millions of homes throughout the world. What better tribute could there be to the two men in whom, for a few hours on a December day, their simple and devout love of God and duty had kindled the flame of genius and from whose collaboration something deathless had been born?

Silent Night

Silent night, holiest night,
Darknesss flies, all is light,
Shepherds hear the Angels sing :
Hallelujah, hail the King,
Jesus, the Saviour is here
Jesus the Saviour is here!

Silent night, holiest night,
Guiding star, lend thy light,
See the Eastern Magi bring,
Gifts and homage to our King,
Jesus, the Saviour is here!
Jesus the Saviour is here.

Silent night, holiest night,
Wond'rous star, lend thy light,
With the Angels let us sing,
Hallelujah to the King.
Jesus, our Saviour is here,
Jesus, our Saviour is here!